inherit the earth

inherit the earth

Stories From
MEXICAN RANCH LIFE

by
ALVIN GORDON

drawings by

THE UNIVERSITY OF ARIZONA PRESS
Tucson, Arizona

About the Author and the Artist

ALVIN GORDON'S concern for intercultural understanding was a prime motive in the writing of this book, as it has been in many of his other activities. As author, actor, and film producer, he has portrayed variously the humanity of man on both sides of international boundaries. Writing and directing for the educational films, he has been at the same time president of Gateway Films in San Francisco and operator of a hotel in Sonora, Mexico.

TED DE GRAZIA, in the brush and ink drawings and the jacket painting, displays two of the numerous techniques that have made him a first-rank Southwestern artist. De Grazia's interpretations of the daily human scene are as well known as his collections of paintings commemorating the lives and works of major religious figures in Arizona, California, and Mexico.

THE UNIVERSITY OF ARIZONA PRESS

First printing 1963
Second printing 1963
Third printing 1969

S. B. N. 8165-0043-6
L. C. No. 63-11977

CONTENTS

THE FAMILY

'APA	
'AMA	
ROSITA	Age Five
PEPE	Age Seven
RAMÓN	Age Eight
SONOQUI	Age Nine
ÁNGELA	Age Ten
MARIANO	Age Eleven
PANCHO	Age Thirteen
BEATRIZ	Age Fourteen

* * *

DON POLO — The ranch owner

INTRODUCTION

The following is a series of incidents in the lives of members of *una familia humilde* (as they would call themselves), "one humble family." The place is almost anywhere in Mexico at the 1500 to 2000 foot level above the sea as the sierra begins its climb to the lofty ridges where the growth of the highlands often meets that of the lowlands. The climate is temperate.

Here live many families who, despite the rapid national drive toward industrialization, mass production, and a solid middle class, either out of preference or circumstance stand in between, emancipated from the bonds of semi-slavery but clinging to the security of the older paternalism.

Such is the family of Juan Lopez. It will probably not be the same for his children, for time marches fast in changing the face of Mexico. But for Juan, 'Apa of eight, such is his lot in life, to be caretaker or mayordomo of a small ranch at the outskirts of an old colonial village long since beyond its glory, by-passed for the moment by the flood of the modern age.

He is given four ancient adobe walls and something of a roof over his head. He is allowed to use some ground to keep a few laying hens, a pig now and again, and he may partake of what grows in the rancho family garden. He is paid only the minimum salary, for the rancho is small and hardly productive.

Most important to him is that he has a position, *mayordomo,* which is based upon the owner's confidence in him and his integrity.

Humility need not exclude honest pride, and he, like countless others in Mexico, is proud of his job and proud of his *familia humilde.*

[9]

THE BIG RAIN

It had been an easy summer. October came with no promise of storms, but intermittent gentle, sustained rainfall had watered the crops to a healthy growth and raised the wells to their normal levels. With the hard rains came erosion and the mud and leaking roofs.

'Apa tilted his chair back against the house wall, lighted the stub of a cigarette and surveyed the early evening sky. One small dark cloud drifted aimlessly over the Sierra.

"No changes there," he thought. "It's been an easy summer."

'Ama came out of the cook-house, the light of day now gone, her chores now done. She stood alongside of 'Apa and followed his stare as the bright first stars came into view.

"We have been lucky," she said. "This old house still stands. We have a roof."

"At least until January," 'Apa replied.

"At least until January," she agreed with a sigh.

"And then if we pass January, then we're fine until July. Think of that."

"I have thought of that, and I hope, and I pray," and she moved into the dark shadows of the house and spread the *petates* — reed mats on the earth floor for the family to sleep upon.

About ten o'clock it began, softly at first like a mist covering the narrow valley in a shroud. Then the dark cloud came closer. Thunder shook the very mountain tops. Lightning flashed and the sky seemed to open up and pour out rivers of water.

'Apa got up and lighted the lantern. He felt along the walls. He knew every weak spot well. So far, it was still holding on the high side, the two hundred-year-old roof — the rotted beams, the stained and mildewed bricks. But for how long? He stepped over the bodies of the sleeping children to the low wall and ran his hand along it. One, two little streams were running down. "Not bad, yet, not bad," he thought. Each year he promised himself to save the money to repair the roof, and each year somehow, when the time came, there was no money at all.

The downpour continued. More rivulets ran to the floor. 'Ama woke up and inspected the sleeping children. She disturbed those sleeping near the low wall, moved their mat next to the high wall. They followed half-asleep, and fell asleep again.

The lantern sputtered, it was leaking in the very center of the room. One of the children lying there cried

out in fear as water hit her face. 'Ama awakened her and the others near her, and they too moved near the high wall.

The entire roof began to leak except a few feet from the high wall. 'Ama and 'Apa moved their few belongings as close to it as they could. Rotten plaster gave way and fell in large chunks. But the children slept soundly through it all.

'Ama and 'Apa stood with their backs against the high wall waiting for the sinking of the beams, more falling plaster, perhaps the whole roof.

Then the rain stopped. They could hear the rush and roar of the muddy waters in the *arroyo* just below, punctuated by intermittent drops that persisted in the room itself.

They opened the door. The sky was clear, the stars were bright, and a new moon lighted the silvery stalks of the wet feed-corn.

"We're all right," said 'Apa almost to himself. "This must be the last."

"It must be," 'Ama answered.

"At least until January."

"At least."

"Perhaps until July, and by then we should have the money . . . "

"Perhaps until July," 'Ama wishfully agreed.

ROSITA AND THE TORTILLA

Rosita made herself sit down on the clean, swept dirt by the door of the cook-house. In her five years she had learned patience for many things, but no matter how hard she tried, when she was hungry, when she heard the pat-pat of her mother's agile hands working over the corn dough, when she smelled the half-sour smell of the local wood burning, the very thought of a fresh hot tortilla pulled at her. Restraint came easier sitting down. But lean forward she did, and as the corn pancake heated on the metal disc, as the familiar odor crept out of the cook-house dominating the wood smoke, she salivated, tasting the finished product.

With eight children to feed and a hard-working husband, her mother countenanced no rushing of the job, each in his turn when she was ready. Her domain was the cook-house, and here she governed with a rigid rule. Disturb her, Rosita knew, and perhaps be the last to eat.

Rosita felt herself creeping closer and closer to the doorway. She put her hands on the ground as though to restrain her forward movements. How much longer she could hold out, she didn't know. Moments went by like minutes, minutes like hours. One by one, her sisters and brothers leisurely formed a loosely knit line behind her. She felt that she was being pushed. Her fingers dug into the dry earth till they hurt.

Then it happened. Her mother's hand reached out holding a fresh, hot tortilla.

She almost snatched it, but this was not allowed. Only animals snatched at food. Carefully she pushed herself up into a standing position. She remembered to dust her hands on her skirt. Then with a tiny but distinct "Gracias, 'Ama,'" she accepted the tortilla. She moved tensely from the front of the line, walked slowly, turned around the corner of the building, and once out of sight, ran with all the speed she could muster to a hidden spot behind a huge tree. Caution made her stop and look to be certain that no one could see her. Then she gobbled the tortilla and ran back to take her place at the end of the line. She was still hungry. The first tortilla whetted her appetite for another. She began to push forward, then remembered, and sat down and once again dug her small fingers hard into the dry earth.

PANCHO AND THE DEER

Pancho lay on his back on the reed mat staring up at the ceiling, the round log beams, the long bricks laid over them. His eyes fastened on deer tracks pressed into one of the bricks when the adobe was first molded and drying in the sun. He imagined the figure of the deer, a large buck with a massive spread of antlers. Tonight, at last, 'Apa was to take him hunting, even perhaps to let him shoot a rifle.

He must sleep now, for he did not want to be tired and hold his father back, and his father was strong and moved very fast. But sleep would not come, and he reviewed the plan for the day. He was to go to Uncle Roberto's house and borrow his single-shot rifle. Then he was to stop at the store and borrow two shells. The rifle and the shells could be paid for in venison, and 'Apa was known to be a lucky and skillful hunter. And finally he fell asleep dreaming of countless huge bucks running by.

"Pancho, Pancho," 'Ama called to awaken him. It is late. The afternoon will soon make it dark. Get up, my son, and hurry on your errands."

He bolted up and ran to the town. It seemed that everyone knew about his forthcoming adventure. He reached Uncle Roberto's house breathless only to find that his uncle was out at the *milpa* — his field — tilling the soil. It was a long way. But no one else would lend so precious a thing as a gun. Indeed Uncle Roberto always had it with him when he went to his *milpa*.

The hot afternoon sun burned at Pancho's body and he slowed down to a dog-trot. It wasn't long before he could hear his uncle's gruff voice shouting at his mules as they pulled the plow through the heavy earth.

His uncle stopped when he saw him and beckoned him to sit beside him in the shade of a mesquite tree.

"Pancho," he told him, "you are about to be introduced into the world of men — of hunters."

Pancho swelled with pride. His uncle had never talked with him this way before, considering him a man.

"Yes," his uncle continued, "but there is one most important thing that you should know."

Pancho waited impatiently while uncle lighted a cigarette.

"When you shoot a deer," uncle went on, "you have to hit him just right."

"And where, where is just right?"

"Just right is not in the head where many persons think."

"It isn't?"

"It's just above the high part of the front leg. Just above the shoulder, so that the bullet goes straight to the heart."

"Straight to the heart," repeated Pancho, hanging on every word.

"Oh, you might kill him through the head, but the risk."

"What, what risk?" Pancho asked.

"Haven't you heard?"

"No."

"He may haunt you, his ghost that is, because while he's down, and he doesn't move, and he doesn't breathe, he's not altogether dead unless it's clean through the heart, and he may haunt you."

"How, just how would he haunt me?"

"Better not to worry about it," uncle advised. "Just be sure and hit him in the only place." And he got up and unfastened the rifle from his saddle and gave it to

Pancho. "Let's just think about a nice juicy barbecue of venison. I can taste it now."

Pancho had hardly time to thank him when he was almost being pushed down the road. "Hurry, my boy, hurry. And the best of luck to you."

Pancho approached the shopkeeper. "I would like," he said, "two shells for this rifle."

"Who's going to do the shooting tonight," he asked, "you or your 'Apa?"

" 'Apa said that I could," Pancho replied.

"You mean you want me to gamble two shells against a piece of meat that you will be responsible for shooting?"

"Well, I thought . . ."

"You thought. But you should know that shells cost plenty of money, and a man should have a little security for his investment."

" 'Apa said I could fire the first one," Pancho stammered, "and that if I miss, he would take the gun."

"That's a promise?" asked the merchant.

"A promise," said Pancho, and the merchant handed him the shells.

"And when you shoot, remember to hit him just above the shoulder and right through the heart, or . . ."

"Yes, I understand, I know," and Pancho scurried home.

Supper was a hurried meal. The entire family was filled with anticipation. Soon there would be meat, first barbecued in their beehive oven, then the remainder cut into strips and steamed dry and pounded with stones into *machaca* — jerky — to be rolled inside tortillas and fried into savory *tacos*.

'Apa checked his big flashlight. The batteries were good — the beam struck out far into the fields. Pancho carried the gun, the two shells jangling in his pocket as

[17]

he trotted along after his father toward the dark of the sierra.

Hours went by as the flashlight's beam intermittently cut through the night in vain. Pancho was tiring.

"A little more," 'Apa encouraged him, "and we'll be at the hollow where the *Palo Santo* grows and the deer come down to eat the sweet white blossoms. Now, we go quietly." They moved in silence.

"Load the gun," 'Apa whispered.

Carefully Pancho put one shell into the rifle.

"Now, get ready."

'Apa moved Pancho in front of him, held the light high, and snapped the button. The bright beam made the white furry clusters on the *Palo Santo* stand out like balls of silver thread. A pair of brilliant tiny mirrors reflected themselves in the light. They were the eyes of a buck, his horns high in the air.

"Take good aim," said 'Apa. "He'll stand still a while. Remember, just above the shoulder."

A shot cut through the silence, the deer stumbled.

"I got him," whispered Pancho. "I got him."

"But only in the leg." The deer began to limp away. "Give me the gun."

" 'Apa, 'Apa, please — please let me try again." Pancho remembered what Uncle Roberto had told him. "Please, 'Apa," he pleaded.

"There is no time." 'Apa took the gun. "Here, hold the light steady." He handed Pancho the flashlight.

'Apa loaded. He aimed and fired. The deer fell, shot through the heart.

'Apa set himself to skinning and cleaning the animal.

"We're not far from home," he said. "We've been circling the hill. Do you think you can find your way and bring a burro?"

The moon was now up, and Pancho felt that he knew.

"Go to the north," said 'Apa, "and you'll hit the road, then turn right."

On the way home Pancho began to wonder how the deer might haunt him. He satisfied himself with the thought that 'Apa had shot him through the heart and that he must be truly dead.

Home was not far. He rode the burro back. They tied the carcass on the little pack animal, and soon were greeted by the family enthusiastically awaiting the victorious hunters.

But when Pancho lay himself down on the straw mat, the flickering lantern illuminated the deer track on the brick above. And when he fell asleep he dreamed that hundreds of huge deer were running upside down on the ceiling above him, ready to fall at any instant.

He woke up terrified. He made his way to the shed. He ran his hand over the suspended carcass of the deer. There was the hole, just above the shoulder. There was no movement, no breath. No, he was dead.

And Pancho went back into the house and fell into a sound sleep.

MARIANO AND THE FISH

Mariano clapped his straw sombrero to his head, walked out to the pasture and mounted a burro. A light haze hid the sun.

"A good day for fishing," he thought as his legs steered the burro along the Camino Real toward the river. Almost every Sunday he would stuff a few tortillas in his pocket, take his precious handline with a small piece of dried meat for bait, and make the same journey. Many a time he returned with nothing to show for his pains, and then he could anticipate the family discussion — the waste of the dried meat, enough for a meal for one person at least — they couldn't afford it. But once in a while he proudly carried a large catfish to his family

— fresh baked fish that very night, very often enough left over to smoke and dry.

For many Sundays he had returned empty-handed.

"This will be a lucky day," his optimism asserted itself as the burro picked his way over the depleted ancient cobblestones, and he whistled a happy tune.

A turn to the left, up over the steep hill, then down the rocky slope, and there was the river quietly moving from shallow ledge to a deep hole, then another ledge, and another deep hole, until it rounded the bend and disappeared.

Mariano tied the burro in a shady spot and waded across the ledge. He baited the hook. He climbed the high rock wall that surrounded the deep hole, and threw the hook into the water. Tensely he waited, hoping for the great moment — that it might happen at once. After a while he sat down and began to nibble on one of the tortillas.

Hours went by. A variety of birds came to drink. A pair of teal frolicked. A huge turtle floated by leisurely. Mariano fell asleep, the end of the line clasped firmly in one hand.

He woke up off balance. A fish, the biggest fish he had ever experienced, was tugging away — pulling him off balance. He tried to steady himself, but there was nothing to hold on to. Just above him was a bush. If he could reach it, he felt sure he could brace himself and hold the big fish. He stretched his free arm out. The fish lay still for a moment. He pulled himself up, straddled the bush, and began to anticipate the glory that would be his when he presented his family with his prize.

Then the fish headed downstream. Mariano held the line with both hands. He felt the bush give way. He began to slide down the rock wall. Into the river he went, down under the water. To save himself he had to let go of the line. He held onto the rock wall with his fingertips, and slowly, hand over hand, made his way to the shallow ledge.

He wanted to cry. Then he saw in the riffles around him hundreds of tiny varicolored fish. Enough of these, he thought, would at least make a meal. He began to scoop up the water with his sombrero, trying to catch them. They were nimble and fast, but at last he had one. He studied it as it swam wild circles in the diminishing water in the sombrero. A beautiful thing of blue and red and yellow. Then, the water was gone, the fish flopped on the wet straw, and the colors disappeared. He dipped more water; the colors returned at once.

Slowly he lowered the sombrero into the stream and watched the little fish escape. He mounted the burro and headed for home realizing that without his hook and line, without fish to eat, it was possible that he might never return to the river.

Somehow, he was not sad. He thought he should be, as he reviewed his situation. But as he listened to the click of the burro's hooves on the cobblestones of the Camino Real, he again began to whistle a happy tune.

SONOQUI

Sonoqui saw the large blue sedan through the dust cloud that shrouded it, as it made the distant curve.

"A tourist," he cried. "It begins. It begins," and he ran to the main house, crouched in the shadow of the high front wall and waited.

Horses were Sonoqui's love, and last year Don Polo had allowed him to rope the horses, to comb and brush them, and to help with the saddling when a tourist came to ride. More than the peso or two which he frequently received as a tip for his efforts, he loved to touch the smooth coats of the horses, to make them clean and shiny, and he relished the smell of fine leather of the bridles and the saddles. He loved to talk to the horses, and they seemed to understand him thoroughly.

Perhaps, more than anything, he loved the feeling of importance; a nine-year-old boy from the house of a low peon receiving thank-yous and courtesies from the important tourists from far away.

The blue car came to a stop at the gate, and the driver blew the horn. Don Polo came out of the house and talked with him. Slowly Sonoqui made his way out of the shadows.

"Come here, Sonoqui," Don Polo beckoned to him. "You have a client for tomorrow at 7 o'clock in the morning, sharp."

Then he spoke in English to the tourist, indicating that Sonoqui would take care of him. Doubt, readable in any language, crossed the tourist's face.

"That little thing, handle a full-grown horse?"

"You bet," said Don Polo as he rumpled Sonoqui's hair. "Best cowboy on the ranch."

Sonoqui glowed in Don Polo's attention, but the

tourist backed up his car, made a turn, and without even a goodbye, drove off.

"Which horse," asked Sonoqui, "will this gentleman ride tomorrow?"

"I think," Don Polo pondered the question, "I think it will be Sansón."

"Sansón!" Sonoqui fairly shouted. "Your very own horse to — to a tourist?"

"He was recommended by an old friend, my boy, a very old friend. He must be a fine horseman and, as you well know, old friends must have nothing but the best." Then he teased Sonoqui. "Is it that you don't want to comb and brush Sansón, could that be the case?" He knew full well that this horse was Sonoqui's idol.

"Oh no, oh no, but — I thought — But if you say, sir. Of course, tomorrow — tomorrow at seven sharp he will be ready."

At dawn Sonoqui ran to the pasture and called to Sansón. From out of the shadow of a large tree he came, shaking his mane and neighing. He followed Sonoqui to the corral and nuzzled him as the small arms stretched to comb and brush him. Standing on a bench, Sonoqui one by one removed the burrs from the long fine tail and brushed it till it shone in the first long rays of the early morning sun. He went to the shed and struggled to lift Don Polo's saddle from the rack and carry it to the corral. Upon the bench again he climbed, and barely managed to throw the heavy tooled leather over the horse's back. He tightened the cinch, adjusted the stirrups to an estimated leg length, and sat down to wait for the blue car.

This time it came in a great hurry. The horn blew before it reached the gate. Don Polo was there at once and exchanged a few words with the tourist. The car swung into reverse, turned sharply, and sped away.

Sonoqui stared after it.

"I'll take off the saddle." Don Polo was at his side.

Sonoqui stifled his tears.

"Here," said Don Polo, holding out a *peso*.

Sonoqui turned away.

"What happened, Sonoqui? What's the matter?"

"The tourist," the boy mumbled.

"He had to leave at once. His wife's sick. They just telephoned him. At least he was decent enough to come to tell us, not like some of them who . . ."

"But . . ." Sonoqui was now in tears.

"But what?" Don Polo put his hand gently on Sonoqui's head.

"But he didn't stop to tell me how nice Sansón looked, how clean, how fine, how handsome!"

Sonoqui ducked out from under Don Polo's hand and ran toward home. He shouted to the wind, almost wailed.

"He didn't *saludarme* — (he didn't even say good morning) — not at all!"

SHE WILL BE BEAUTIFUL

The party dress was almost finished. The bright red cloth 'Ama had carefully saved for Beatriz's first dance. Now the day had arrived.

"She will be beautiful," thought Beatriz's younger sister, Ángela.

But there was no more red thread. Every centavo the mother had saved had gone to purchase the large white buttons that decorated the front. And no more red thread.

Other colors were suggested and studied only to be rejected. Buying the thread was out of the question, borrowing it at this late date almost impossible. We will find the money in the next few weeks, 'Ama consoled her, and at the next dance . . . But Beatriz, fourteen years old, brimming with the enthusiasm of her young womanhood, anticipating the excitement of the music, the movement, the contact with boys, burst into tears.

Ángela ran to the chicken coop. There were hardly enough eggs these days to feed one to each member of the family daily, but she would do without hers tomorrow. She found an egg, and hurried into town.

Dusk had fallen and with it a silence that foretold the great event, the *baile* that would rouse the whole community later in the night. She hurried from one shop to another, but they were all closed.

She tapped at the door of the residence of one of the shopkeepers.

"*Pase,*" she heard from within, and timidly she moved across the threshold. "*Pase, por que no pasa?*" an annoyed voice shouted at her. Reluctantly she moved forward a few more steps.

The shopkeeper saw her.

"Well," he looked up from his newspaper. "What do you want?"

Ángela could hardly speak.

"Talk up, girl!" The shopkeeper spat out the words. "I haven't got all night. Talk up!"

Then the words rushed out of Ángela like a torrent.

"I have an egg. My sister is beautiful in her party dress. It is almost finished. It is made of a beautiful red cloth, and 'Ama spent all our money on the buttons, and . . ." She stopped to take a breath.

"And what does this mean to me? Why am I to be so disturbed?"

"Don't you understand?"

"Understand what?"

"I need some red thread, and I have an egg."

The shopkeeper stood up and slapped the newspaper down on the chair.

"Come on then, Pug-nose. Let's hurry. The dance

will begin all too soon." And he led her to the shop through the back entry and gave her the thread.

She offered the egg in return.

"No," said the shopkeeper. "Tell your sister Beatriz that an old admirer only wants to look at her tonight."

"She will be beautiful," Ángela replied.

"Yes," said the shopkeeper, remembering years gone by when as a young swain a dance was the greatest event in life. And the girls! Had there been one in a red dress? "Perhaps?" he thought.

"*Con su permiso,*" Ángela murmured, anxious to get away.

"*Ándale, ándale,*" he said, and he went back to his chair, and sat down and searched his memory.

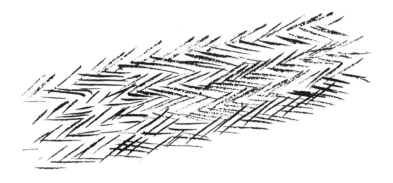

PEPE AND DINAMITA

Pepe woke up with a start. He listened intently, for some foreign sound that might have disturbed his sleep. It was not quite dawn. Moonlight still spilled into the narrow room through the cracks in the doors and windows.

Pepe usually was the last in the family to get up. He ran so hard all day. 'Ama and 'Apa were forever after him to slow down. Even the doctor, to whom Don Polo had taken him, had told him with somber words, after his long siege of coughing and spitting and feeling weak, to take things easy — never run. But running was in his blood. The exhilaration of listening to the wind whistle by his ears, of seeing the cactus, the trees, the rocks, everything around him disappear as he raced by — these made a slow pace unbearable. He lay beside two of his brothers on the straw mat, and listened.

The quail were calling to each other as they gorged themselves on the fallen feed-corn kernels. The cocks were crowing, not only those at the rancho itself, but from the town below they could be heard distinctly. A dog barked and was answered by another. A burro brayed. These were all sounds to which Pepe was accustomed. "Perhaps," he thought, "perhaps they're a little more together, at once, than usual. Perhaps this woke me up."

A horse neighed, just outside the adobe hut, and then neighed again. Pepe recognized the neigh. "Dinamita! But what's he doing here at this time of day? Why isn't he with the others in the pasture?"

Carefully Pepe separated himself from his two brothers and went outside. He shivered for a moment as the pre-dawn chill of early autumn struck him. Dinamita neighed again and pawed the ground. In the half-light his coat looked sleek, his muscles taut.

Dinamita was an old horse, the oldest on the rancho. He was only used for short rides for tourists who wanted to rent a slow, gentle animal. But Pepe remembered his father's stories well. Dinamita had been Don Polo's favorite horse, faster than all the horses in town or from the other ranches. Holiday after holiday he had helped some young rider spear the ring in the contest and win the right to dance with the town queen. But in later years he moved slowly, puffing and wincing on downhill grades, picking his way as carefully as a mule.

Now as Pepe watched him, he looked young again, wanting to run over the valley. Excitement took hold of Pepe. He could not run as much as he liked, but Dinamita would be his legs — Dinamita would carry him into ecstasy. As he walked to the edge of the porch, the horse sidled up to him. He mounted. The usual slow, studied gait carried him beyond the fence out onto the road. Then, as if struck by lightning, the horse ran, the cactus flew by, the trees, the houses, the whole world was set into motion. Chickens scampered, dogs hugged the road edges, and Dinamita ran. For some ten minutes his pace didn't falter. Then he stopped and turned, and with tremendous difficulty made his way home.

When he reached the house his breathing was hard and irregular. Just as Pepe dismounted, Dinamita slowly sank to the ground and rolled over on his side.

"Sleep. Sleep well, Dinamita," Pepe whispered in his ear, "and perhaps tomorrow . . ." Dinamita lay absolutely still.

Quietly Pepe made his way back to the mat. He listened to the quail and the cocks and the dogs and the burros. He watched the moonlight disappear and the sun's first rays burn through the cracks in the door and the windows, and he fell asleep wondering if "tomorrow" was today, or the next day, or the next.

RAMÓN'S FORTUNE

Ramón decided that today was the day that he was going to make a fortune. He had made a careful selection of the gifts that he would purchase for the whole family. A new, bright blue *rebozo* for 'Ama, a fine, stout axe handle for 'Apa, and many other things for his seven brothers and sisters; and for himself, the largest pig made of *cajeta* (quince jelly paste) that money could buy.

He went to the shed and borrowed a feed sack, and started out for the foothills where the quince grew in abundance. He would fill the sack with ripe quince, at least as many as his small body could carry. He would sell them to Tia Carmelita, for she was known all over as the finest maker of quince paste in the entire town or countryside. And then, he would buy the gifts and come home like the Three Kings came to the Baby Christ.

The first trees he came to had already been picked bare. Further and further he went, finding only one piece of fruit here, another there, until he realized that he had gone far enough from home, that the sun was already halfway down below the craggy mountain peak.

With the small quantity of fruit, his dreams of generosity diminished. "Perhaps," he thought, "I can trade with Tia Carmelita, at least for a small strip of the sweet?"

The Tia's house was a busy place. Great cauldrons were bubbling over with the boiling fruit and sugar mix. Molds in a variety of shapes and forms lay on a long table ready to receive the hot mix.

In the next room the finished wares were displayed. Cats, and dogs, and flowers, and fruits, all of the golden brown jelly.

Ramón spotted a huge pig, almost a meter long. This had been his dream — but alongside it he saw a tiny one,

with a curly tail. This was a possibility. He studied it carefully. "If anything," he thought, "it's even nicer than the big pig, and it looks funnier."

Tia had not noticed Ramón, so occupied was she in directing the activities. Now she saw him.

"*Buenas tardes*," she said.

"*Buenas tardes*," he replied.

"Been gathering fruit, my little one?"

"Yes," Ramón replied hesitantly.

"Any luck?"

"Only . . . only a little," and he handed her the almost empty sack.

She rolled the fruit out into a bin.

"And how much do you think these are worth, young man?"

"I thought," murmured Ramón, "I thought I might ask you for a pig. Not the big pig," he added hastily, "but the little tiniest one." And he pointed to the funny figure.

"Not much fruit," said Tia. She picked a quince up in her hand and surveyed it. "Prime quality, however, prime quality, and that's all we use in our *cajeta*. Yes, Ramón, yes, I believe that's worth a tiny pig. Take it, my boy, take it — then, off with you. I'm a busy woman, can't you see?"

Ramón picked up the little pig and laid it out on his palm. The sweet odors of the cooking had made him famished. Down the street, he could resist no longer. He studied his prize.

"He will still be a pig without the tail," he thought. So he ate the tail, and it was very good. He went a few more blocks. "It will still look like a pig without the hind part," he was sure. So he ate the hind part.

At the outskirts of town, he stopped again. "From the head alone, anyone would know it is a pig." And he ate everything, but the head.

Then, it seemed rather silly, indeed, to come home with only the head of a pig. So he ate that too.

And as he entered the gate to the rancho, he determined that next year he would start looking for quince much, much sooner, long before others came to pick. And he would make a fortune, and buy his mother a bright blue *rebozo,* and his father a new stout axe handle, and lots of wonderful things for his sisters and his brothers. And for himself (he wondered how he would carry it home), the great huge *cajeta* pig.

THE TELEPHONE CALL

"Pepe! Pepe!" a woman's voice called out across the Plaza.

Pepe was on his way home from school. He stopped and searched with his eyes. Could this be the teacher? And what had he done?

"You want me?" he shouted.

The telephone operator motioned for him to come closer.

"There's a telephone call for your father. Hurry home and tell him."

Pepe was out of earshot before she finished speaking. "A telephone call? A telephone call?" No one in his family ever received telephone calls.

When he got to the rancho he found his father busy hoeing the soil. He was so out of breath he couldn't talk.

"What is it, my boy. What is it? Have you seen the ghost of the old Jesuit padre?"

"No, no," Pepe sputtered. "It's that . . . that there is . . ."

"There is what? Now calm down, my son, and tell me."

"There is a telephone call for you."

"For me?"

"Of course, for you. The operator told me in the Plaza to hurry home and get you."

"For me, Juan Lopez?"

"It must be!"

'Apa dropped his hoe and ran to the house.

" 'Ama, 'Ama, hurry! A bath, a fresh shirt, my suit."

'Ama's face turned ashen. She was afraid to ask the obvious question.

"No, nobody died," said 'Apa. "It's not a funeral. Nobody died."

"Well . . .?"

"There's a telephone call for me." 'Apa tried to toss it off lightly.

"For you?" Several of the children joined 'Ama.

"Are you certain you are the right Juan Lopez?" 'Ama asked.

"Of course," replied 'Apa, now gaining self-assurance.

One of the children put the *olla* on the fire for bath water, one heated the iron to press the shirt, one started to shine 'Apa's shoes. 'Apa stripped off his clothes, and let himself be bathed by his family.

Then he shaved and dressed, put on his best hat, and went to town.

"Buenas tardes, Juan Lopez," the operator greeted him.

"Buenas tardes," he replied, removing his hat. "You wanted me?"

"Someone wanted you. Now let me see?" She devoted herself to the small wooden console switchboard. She turned the handle briskly again and again.

"They are always asleep. Always," she remarked to herself. "*Bueno! Bueno!* Yes, here is Juan Lopez, ready to talk."

'Apa leaned over the operator's shoulder and shouted into the switchboard, "*Bueno!*"

"No, no no," the operator admonished him. "Here," she handed him the receiver. He held it at arm's length and shouted even louder, "*Bueno!*"

"No, Señor Lopez, no. *Con su permiso.*" She held the receiver to his ear in its proper position.

"*Bueno!*" again he shouted.

Gently she took the receiver from him, softly she spoke to the party at the other end of the line.

"You see, this is the first time Señor Lopez has talked on the telephone.

"What?"

"Yes, that's why I told you when you called that it could not be the Juan Lopez you were looking for. Gracias," and she hung the phone on its hook.

She turned to 'Apa.

"I am sorry," she said, "for molesting you. I told them it could not be this Juan Lopez that they wanted."

"Gracias." Slowly 'Apa put his best hat on his head and turned away. "Gracias. No, it could not possibly be this Juan Lopez, not possibly. Gracias, *buenas tardes.*"

Sadly he moved on down the street.

SHOESHINE BOY

For his birthday, Don Polo had given Ramón the materials for a shoeshine kit. 'Apa built the wooden box and fixed a leather handle to it.

Ramón spent his every spare moment at the Plaza or the Alameda near the market watching the boys who made shining shoes their profession. He would become, he was certain, the best shoeshine boy in the whole town.

Don Polo gave him the pastes and the brushes and the cloths, and explained how to use them. Ramón practised on 'Apa's one pair of shoes until they shone like mirrors.

'Ama made him a neat outfit of blue pants and a khaki shirt which was to be worn only after school for the express purpose of carrying on his trade.

On his way to and from school each day Ramón passed the tourist hotel, and had become acquainted with the manager. Sometimes there were errands to run, for the hotel would soon reopen for the season. He liked to run the errands, just to feel the importance of being part of this great establishment, and every now and again he got fifty centavos or even a peso for his efforts.

Proudly he told the manager of his new venture, and the manager suggested that he come to the hotel every evening at six o'clock and be the official shoeshine boy.

Then the manager gave him a large cloth and explained that he should spread the cloth out on the floor and put all his utensils and pastes on it so as not to stain the tiles; that he must always present himself on time, and be neat and clean and have his hair well-combed.

The day arrived when the hotel reopened. 'Ama cleaned and polished and combed him, and off he went carrying his brand-new shine box with him.

At a quarter of six he was at the hotel — but now that the place was occupied he was afraid to enter.

The manager spotted him and beckoned him in. He led him to a corner of the patio where he sat himself on the box and waited.

A trio of musicians arrived. The spotlight was turned on, and the music began. Slowly the guests came out of their rooms and made themselves comfortable in the arcade, some selecting big straight chairs, others rockers.

Ramón was afraid to make his presence known. He had never before been this close to *gente de razón,* important people. He studied their clothes, clean, well-cut, very very important looking. And as his eyes moved down he was struck by the fact that they all wore shoes, and that he, he alone, was barefoot.

He plotted his escape. He waited until the spotlight was turned off, then quietly picked his way across the patio and toward the exit.

"Shine!" a voice called out. His heart sank. He had to be polite.

"Shine!" and a man motioned him to come over. He sucked in his stomach to let his trousers fall to cover his bare feet, and he moved toward the man.

He tucked his feet under him and sat on them. He laid out the cloth. He spread his equipment on it. He propped the box under the man's right foot and began to follow the procedure which he had studied and practised so well.

And as the shoe began to sparkle in the candlelight, as he whipped the cloth across, again and again, his fear left him and a dream took its place. He would work hard, every evening. A peso a shine. He did not know how much a pair of shoes would cost, but he had confidence that it would not be too long before he could buy them.

THE PIÑATA

Every Christmas Don Polo provided the family with the materials for the construction of a *piñata*. This year they had decided that it would take the form of a burro.

Sundays were devoted to this enterprise: Forming the skeleton of wire attached to the clay pot that was the center of the body; then cutting strips of vari-colored paper and pasting them on, layer by layer.

Christmas morning, Don Polo brought candies and peanuts and these were stuffed into the pot, and finally the opening was sealed up.

One end of a long rope had been tied to a tree, and 'Apa climbed to the top of the shed holding the other end of it. The *piñata* burro was suspended from the middle.

Before the first hitter was blindfolded, the real burro Matilda came forward and nuzzled the *piñata*.

"You see," cried 'Ama. "We have built a *piñata* so real looking that Matilda thinks it might be her own child," and everyone laughed but Ángela.

Suddenly, to her, the *piñata* became real, became alive. She envisioned the paper animal nursing at Matilda, walking its first unstable steps, braying its first cries of life. She did not want to see it smashed with the stick.

Sonoqui was now blindfolded, stick in hand. They turned him around three times. 'Apa swung the *piñata* high over his head. Then he lowered it so that it brushed Sonoqui's forehead. Sonoqui struck at it and missed.

Ángela held her hands over Matilda's eyes. Again and again, contestants swung and missed, and Ángela kept Matilda's eyes covered.

Then it was her turn. With mixed emotions she held back, but the urgings of the other members of her family, the excitement of the contest, finally won her over.

"I won't hit him, I won't," she whispered to Matilda. Then she subjected herself to the blindfold and the three turns around.

'Apa let the *piñata* tickle her forehead. He lowered it right in front of her.

"Hit it! Hit it! Now, now!" her brothers and sisters, hungry for the candy and nuts, encouraged her. But she delayed as long as she could. Then, when she felt certain that it was nowhere near her, she swung, and to her surprise smashed the *piñata* into bits.

She ripped off her blindfold as tears began to fill her eyes. She was about to apologize to Matilda, when she caught sight of the burro pushing her way into the scrambled crowd of youngsters searching out candies and peanuts. And Ángela laughed, and with a great scream of joy she dove headlong into the melee and grabbed for her rightful share of the treasures.

THE BOXER

For several weeks, 'Apa had been teaching Pancho how to box. 'Apa had told him many times how, when he was Pancho's age, he had outboxed every boy in town including the massive El Gordo. Over and over again the boys would match little slight 'Apa against El Gordo for the sheer fun of seeing El Gordo lose.

Now El Gordo's boy, a replica of his father, this very Friday night had challenged all comers, and 'Apa had taken up the challenge in the name of Pancho. Normally, Gordo's boy and Pancho were good friends. They played together, took hikes together, sat beside each other at school. But for the past few weeks, their fathers had kept the boys separate from one another and tried to develop animosity between them.

Now it was Friday. The old roofless ruin where the matches were held was crowded with contemporaries of 'Apa and El Gordo, desirous of seeing a reenactment of old times.

When Pancho faced young Gordo in the ring, when he looked up at his squinting eyes and scowling mouth, when he saw the wide span of his broad chest and the long heavy arms extending from his broad shoulders, he was frightened.

The bell rang.

"Remember what I told you," yelled 'Apa. "Hit him in the nose, right on the nose. That's the way I beat his old man time after time."

Pancho saw a mountain of flesh and two huge gloves coming at him. He ducked, and dodged, and feinted, and ran backwards, until the crowd roared for action and began to hoot and call him insulting names.

The bell rang, and he was glad.

"Hit him, right on the nose," pleaded 'Apa. "Right on the nose."

Round Two began. Pancho closed his eyes and ran forward, arms outstretched before him, and he hit something hard. He opened his eyes, and saw blood spurting from his opponent's nose. The referee stopped the bout, and Pancho was acclaimed the winner.

"What did I tell you, my boy!" 'Apa embraced him as he climbed out of the ropes. "Right on the nose!" 'Apa unlaced the gloves.

The cheers of the crowd still rang in Pancho's ears, and he bit hard on his lower lip to stem the tide of tears. He had hurt his friend. He had made him bleed. He ran out of the building.

CONFETTI

For months, the whole family had been saving eggshells. 'Ama was expert at chopping the small end off the egg, leaving just enough space for the yoke to fall through. Then the shells were hung on the roof to dry, until a few weeks before Feria — Carnival — the whole roof was covered with eggshells.

Colored paper and glue and dyes had been purchased on credit. All the children helped cut the paper into confetti to stuff the eggshells. Then a small piece of paper was glued over the hole and the egg was dyed blue, or yellow, or green.

There was a dance, of course, at Carnival, but the most fun was throwing those decorated egg shells — *cascarones* — at one another, breaking them over another's head and watching the confetti, like colored rain drops, explode all over.

When the day of Carnival came, the family had almost four hundred *cascarones* prepared for sale at five centavos apiece. Two wheelbarrows full were pushed along the lane and into the center of town to the Plaza.

As the music from the dance at the Town Hall carried out to the Plaza, the sale became brisk and the Plaza itself was a cloud of confetti muffling the happy and surprised shouts of the youngsters.

Pepe watched this from his post by a wheelbarrow. If only he could throw one *cascarón* — have the fun of watching it smash against somebody, of seeing the colorful explosion! But every one was worth five centavos, and even selling them all, all four hundred, what with the cost of the paper and glue and dye there would be barely twelve pesos left.

All but three had been sold. Pepe fingered one of the

remaining ones. He picked it up. A friend of his ran by. He feinted throwing it, then slowly passed it to a purchaser along with the other two in exchange for fifteen centavos.

As he crossed the Plaza on his way home, Pepe saw a *cascarón* coming at him in the air. He ripped off his hat and snared it. It was not broken, and it was his. He was tempted to throw it at the first person passing, then he thought of 'Apa, thought of the wonderful way he smiled and laughed at the little jokes the children played on him. He decided to wait.

At home, 'Apa and 'Ama were sitting outside, waiting. The children turned over their money to 'Ama. Pepe waited until all were intent upon counting the receipts. Then he walked up behind 'Apa, and was about to . . . But one of his brothers saw him, saw the egg in his hand, and scolded him for not selling it.

Pepe protested, and finally was able to explain what happened.

"You are sure," asked 'Apa, "that you are telling the truth?"

"Please, please believe me," Pepe pleaded, angry and sad at being falsely accused.

"You have never lied to me," said 'Apa. "Never."

Then Pepe did it. He smashed the *cascarón* on 'Apa's head, and the confetti scattered in his hair, on his shoulders, and all over him. 'Apa stood up and did a little crazy dance, scattering the bits of paper in every direction. Then he picked Pepe up and swung him around, and both of them fell to the ground and rolled over, laughing.

THE MIRACLE

The day of the patron saint of the big church in town was soon to come. Every year, each *barrio* or section of town honored its own saint by building a float depicting the saint's attributes. Each night, the residents of a different *barrio* paraded behind their float. And on the final night all floats joined into a massive parade which ended at the big church.

The *barrio* in which the Lopez family was included had as its saint Our Lady of Lourdes, the saint of miracles. The owner of the general store had a colored reproduction of a painting of the saint standing in front of a small grotto with the young girl, Bernadette, kneeling before her and offering her the rosary.

The shopkeeper had volunteered his truck, and all hands busied themselves reproducing the setting on a grand scale on the truck bed.

Ángela had been selected to portray Bernadette, and 'Ama carefully cut and stitched her outfit. This was indeed a great honor that the *barrio* had extended to the Lopez family, and Ángela swelled with pride as she contemplated being driven through the streets and being looked upon with awe and envy.

The big day came. The last-minute touches, and by evening the scene was ready for the actors to take their places.

The shopkeeper's daughter, portraying the saint in a flowing white gown, a blue sash, and with a gilt halo upon her head, took her position in the mouth of the grotto. Ángela knelt before her, her little hands holding out the rosary.

But the truck wouldn't start. Something was wrong with the motor. The men swarmed around while the shopkeeper investigated. The starter worked, so it wasn't a dead battery. Someone suggested the possibility of there being no gasoline; and although the shopkeeper resented this implication of his stupidity, he condescended to check, and found it to be true!

A young volunteer was sent posthaste to get a jugful of gas.

Ángela's knees began to hurt. Her arms were slowly drooping. She caught herself as the rosary touched the floor, and straightened up. It seemed like hours before gasoline was put into the truck and the engine started. She felt that she could hold her position no longer. Her entire body quivered.

Then the firecrackers began to go off. The truck moved slowly over the cobblestoned street. The procession formed behind it. And a new strength from out of nowhere came to Ángela. Her body regained its composure, her knees no longer hurt. Her arms held out the rosary with ease.

"Perhaps I am the little girl in the picture, she thought. Perhaps I have received a miracle."

THE CAPITAL

Sonoqui was always getting hurt. He could not be made to understand that he was unable to keep up with boys three or four years his senior. He tried not only to keep up with their pace but also even to outdo them. And the results were often disastrous. Don Polo's first-aid kit was in frequent use.

Fortunately none of the past injuries had been serious, but now, as he stumbled to the door of Don Polo's house, he could hardly see, for the blood was pouring from his left eye. It was the fault of one loose rock in the roadway. He had been racing two older boys, and almost winning, when he tripped on that loose rock and fell hard, banging his forehead against another stone.

Don Polo cleaned the wound, and was at once impressed with the possible serious consequences. He led Sonoqui to his car, and called back to his wife, "I am taking him to the Capital at once. There is a specialist there. We won't be back before dark."

The Capital? Sonoqui had never been, nor had any other members of his family. The eye hurt, yes, and it was hard to keep the other one open, but maybe it was worth it. After all, a trip to the Capital didn't happen every day.

"At the Capital," Don Polo told him, "you will see the Cathedral, the University, the big office buildings of the state, and many automobiles and many people. It is very, very impressive."

Sonoqui let his uninjured eye close in order to save it for the wondrous sights ahead, and soon he was fast asleep.

Don Polo awakened him when they arrived at the doctor's office, and gently led him in.

The examination was brief. Sonoqui gritted his teeth and held his little fists tightly together as the doctor stitched the torn flesh. The eye itself was injured but would cure, was the doctor's verdict, but there must be no strain on it whatsoever. He wound mounds of bandage around Sonoqui's head.

Back in the car the bandage slipped and covered both eyes and Sonoqui, exhausted by the ordeal, again relaxed into sleep. When he awoke it was dark, and they were nearly home.

'Ama was waiting at the gate and was quickly assured by Don Polo that all was well. At home, the rest of the family pounded Sonoqui with questions.

"How was the Capital?"

"Tell us all about it."

Sonoqui remembered Don Polo's words.

"At the Capital," he said as though he had really seen them, "you see the Cathedral, the University, the big office buildings of the state, and many automobiles and many people. It is very, very impressive."

THE FERIA

Part I — The Ferris Wheel

Once a year the feria, the Carnival, came to town, bringing with it noisy generators that created brilliant flickering lights, brash canned music, and excitement of all kinds.

The children were permitted to go together early on Saturday evening.

A group of boys had gathered around the Ferris wheel, Ramón among them, watching the wondrous undulating movement of the suspended carts — each one of them dreaming of the chance to get aboard and experience this thrilling sensation.

To stimulate interest, numbers had been passed out to the spectators, and a drawing would soon be held. To the lucky winner went a free ride. But the boys were restless. Their bodies empathetically began to imitate the movements of the carts. Soon, with no direction or leadership whatsoever, they emulated the sinuous movement. They formed a circle and ran around and around, falling, rising, laughing. They were no longer copying the wheel. They had created a Ferris wheel made of themselves, and the sensation was sweet and satisfying.

They slowed down as the wheel slowed down, and they stopped, frozen in various stances, when it stopped.

The operator called out the lucky number. Ramón was the winner. He could hardly sustain himself in the flood of his companions' envious eyes as he got into a cart and waited for the machinery to grind.

The music blared louder, the wheel began to turn. Faster and faster. And Ramón anticipated the great thrill. But it did not come. He told himself that he was a lucky one, that only he of all his friends had this chance.

That it was, as his 'Ama would say, "Once in your life."

But somehow, as he looked down at the boys again forming their own circle, he wanted to be back with them, falling, and rising, and laughing.

Part II — The Shooting Gallery

Pancho was intrigued with the shooting gallery. It was presided over by a huge fat man wearing blue jeans with nothing but an undershirt above. His pig-like eyes were shaded by a cracked green plastic visor, but behind him were the treasures. One row of various brands of cheap cigarettes, one row of small animals of clay, and, on top and farther back, lovely dolls gaily dressed in various typical costumes of the country.

Business was slow.

"Twenty centavos a shot," the pig-eyed fat man rasped. "Twenty centavos, and the skillful man can go home with a treasure."

He cocked an air rifle, loaded the muzzle with a cork, and extended it to one onlooker who refused it.

"Tell you what I'll do," he continued. "I'll give every winner one free shot." No one responded. "I'll give every winner one free shot," his irritated voice repeated.

Then he signaled out Pancho.

"Even a kid can win," he said. "I'm gonna show you all. Even a kid can win." He placed the rifle in Pancho's hands. "Now watch."

Pancho aimed at a pack of cigarettes, and fired. The fat man was about to pull a concealed string and tip the pack of cigarettes over, when he saw it fall. His little eyes blinked.

"See that!" he yelled at the crowd. "Just what I told you. Even a kid can do it."

[53]

He handed Pancho the cigarettes.

"Let's see what he does on the next shot!" a bystander called out as he saw the fat man reach for the rifle.

"What next shot?"

"The one you promised!"

"But he didn't even pay for the first one," the fat man sputtered.

A crowd gathered quickly. A murmur, as one informed the other. Then pressure.

"Give him his free shot," voices threatened.

"O.K. O.K. A free shot to every winner." The fat man calmed the group, confident that Pancho's first try was sheer luck. "I am a man of my word."

Pancho aimed at a clay dog, and hit it.

The crowd cheered. "Free shot! Free shot!"

Pancho continued. Cigarettes, trophies, finally one of the big dolls he won, and passed over to his sisters and brothers.

"Enough! Enough!" cried the fat man, and he turned off his lights and closed the shop.

The family stood admiring the winnings. Rosita embraced the doll.

The fat man came 'round to Pancho.

"Son," he said, his little eyes cast down in pathos. "Son — and I know you are a good son to your father — do you want a whole family to starve to death? Do you want to go home tonight, and lie down, and think of a poor mother and father and twelve children lying on the hard cold iron bed of that old truck, hungry; knowing — ah! this is the important thing — knowing that you, and you alone, caused this horrible grief? Do you? Tell me honestly, do you?" He pulled a dirty red handkerchief out of his pocket and blew his nose and wiped his eyes.

"Well, I . . . I . . . ." Pancho stammered.

"I knew you were a good son," the fat man went on. "Knew it all the time." Quickly he snatched the trophies from the children and pushed them behind the counter.

Rosita turned her back to hide the doll. She had never had a doll before. Some of her little friends had them, and now this was hers. Her own brother had given it to her, and she wasn't going to relinquish it.

"Here, little girl," the man laid a pudgy hand on her shoulder. Gently, but insistently, he began to pull the doll away from Rosita. Then she lifted her pleading face up to him, her wide eyes wondering.

His eyes met hers. His fingers loosened their grip. "I always was a soft-hearted *estúpido,*" he murmured. And he released the doll, and turned away.

He wiggled his great hulking body back into the stand. He switched on the lights. He replaced the trophies.

"Twenty centavos a shot," he cried out. "Only twenty centavos a shot, and a skillful man can win . . ."

[55]

FERIA

Part III — Love Goes Around

Beatriz, being the oldest, felt responsible for the rest of the children. She stood apart and watched them. She held Rosita's hand so that she would not get lost in the evening crowd.

But as her eyes wandered, she noticed Octavio, the boy who had claimed her at the dance, and danced with her again and again.

She admired his stance, straight and tall for his fifteen years. She remembered the touch of his hand upon her back as he led her on the dance floor. She remembered the slight difficulty she had had, holding her budding young body correctly apart from his.

Then he saw her. She was standing near an almost homemade entertainment device. A tall pole was its center. Cables dropped from it, and there was a plank seat and straps to secure the rider at the end of each cable. Rosita loved to watch it whirl around, causing the riders to fly in the air and bump each other gently from time to time. So it was here that Beatriz was standing when Octavio saw her.

She hoped he would speak to her, and he did.

"Would you like a ride on that?" he asked. "I have the money for tickets."

"It's such a foolish way to spend your money," Beatriz replied modestly.

"But if you would like it?"

Beatriz watched the contraption turn. She heard one young girl titter and half-scream and reach for a young boy riding in front of her.

"If you're sure *you* would like it," she said.

[57]

"I would like it very much." Octavio tried to hide his enthusiasm.

"Ángela," she called to her sister. "Take care of Rosita for a little while."

Octavio bought the tickets and helped Beatriz into a seat, then buckled himself into the one just behind her.

They began to turn to the music of a Viennese waltz. Octavio adjusted his weight to move himself close to Beatriz. He put his hands on her arms, and they sailed through the air together. The machine gained speed. She grabbed for the cable to steady herself. His hands slipped down, just whisking by her breasts. She shivered and pulled herself away, and they rode separately. Then she knew she wanted him near her. That she was in love. She bent her body back in an attempt to slow herself down. But he moved away, embarrassed by his accidental intimacy.

Then the movement stopped. Quickly he dismounted and helped her down.

Her dream of love and romance and marriage was interrupted by the opening of the curtain of a puppet show. She looked in. Twenty-six puppet *mariachis* were accompanying a Mexican star singing *Bésame mucho.* For a fleeting second she wondered, was it love and marriage that she wanted or was it a career, to be a famous star? Then the curtain fell shut.

Rosita came to her and felt for her hand. Beatriz looked down at her baby sister cuddling the giant doll.

"Thank you," she said to Octavio, holding herself primly erect with great dignity. "Thank you very much. And now, with your permission, I must gather up my children and take them home. It is late."

And on the way, she knew that her place was with

her mother and father and sisters and brothers. She knew she would be with them for at least a year or two, and she was warm and comfortable. But she could still feel the touch of Octavio's hands, so light that she was not certain that it had really occurred.

THE NEW DOG

Mariano rode the burro toward the hills. He was to gather firewood. He came to a large area covered with dead and half-dead manzanita. Here he dismounted, let the burro feed on the sparse greenery, and hacked away with his *machete*. His trained eye estimated the pile of sticks that he had been gathering, and he knew it was all that the burro could carry. With remarkable skill he balanced the load over the burro's back and started down the trail.

He felt that he was being followed. He turned, and there was a young dog, black and white and with floppy ears that indicated at least a slight strain of pointer or setter or spaniel.

"Go home," he spoke to the dog. "Go home before you get lost."

Then he realized that no one lived close by. He observed the dog more carefully. He knew he was hungry, and probably had been abandoned. The dog came up and nuzzled him.

"Where do you come from?" Mariano asked. "How far from here do you live?"

The dog licked his hand.

"You look like a nice dog," Mariano continued. "A very nice dog. Maybe even a hunting dog, perhaps?"

He began to think of having a fine, trained dog all of his own. He had watched Don Polo work with his dog, Lobo and was sure that with patience and kindness he, too, could train a dog.

But he knew that 'Ama and 'Apa would never permit it. Food was hard enough for the family to come by. 'Apa would insult the dog, call him the worst kind of mongrel — unless he were a hunter, and who could tell in a puppy so young. Only recently had Mariano begun to resist the appeal of stray animals, only after many scoldings and finally a spanking.

"I hope with all my heart you have a home." Mariano forced himself to take a stand. "Now, go," and he pushed the puppy away.

But the dog refused to budge. Mariano clapped his hands. The dog ran a few feet, then stopped and turned. He questioned Mariano with beseeching eyes.

Mariano picked up a small stone, not to hit the dog, but to frighten him and send him on his way. He threw it. The puppy was after it in a bound, scooped it in his mouth, and returned to drop it at Mariano's feet.

"You are! You are a hunting dog!" the boy shouted. "A real one, if I ever saw one. Perhaps . . .?"

He patted the burro on the rump and began to walk beside him, knowing now that he was being followed.

It was dusk when he got home. He carried the dog into the shed.

"Now, quiet," he said. "Stay very quiet, and I'll try to think up a way to keep you."

He unloaded the burro and put him to pasture. He went back of the house and removed a piece of dry meat from the line where it was hanging.

He opened the shed door, handed the meat to the grateful dog, and warned him again, "Not a sound out of you. Do you hear? Not a sound." Then he closed the door and went into supper.

Mariano watched 'Apa carefully. He was not in a good mood. Things had gone wrong all day with the pump, and the new parts had not come from the city. Soon they would be out of water and the planted things would dry up and die. No, Mariano was sure this was no time to speak to 'Apa about keeping the dog.

A mournful cry cut through the night.

"What was that?" 'Ama asked.

"Just a dog," 'Apa replied.

Mariano laid down his tortilla.

Another cry.

"He sounds as though he is being hurt." 'Ama sympathized.

'Apa's eyes searched his family. At the next cry, he knew that a dog was locked in the shed, and that Mariano had put him there. Without a word, he picked up the lantern and went outside.

Mariano trembled. He could sense the harshness of his father's words, feel the sting of his solid hand on the seat of his pants. Slowly he followed 'Apa, always keeping his distance.

'Apa opened the shed door. The puppy ran forward, expecting another piece of meat.

"Now go," said 'Apa, "get out of here right now, before I kick you so hard that you may never come back to earth."

Mariano knew that 'Apa would never do such a thing, but his words made him shudder.

The dog trembled, moved away, then turned and looked up at 'Apa.

'Apa picked up a stone and rolled it at the dog. Quickly he snatched it and dropped it at 'Apa's feet. 'Apa tried it again, and once more the dog brought the stone back to him. 'Apa picked up the dog, put him in the shed, and locked the door.

Mariano ran for the house.

'Apa went to the back, took some of the dried meat, returned to the shed, fed the puppy, and bedded him down on an old saddle blanket.

Then he went back to the house.

"What was it?" 'Ama asked.

'Apa stared straight at Mariano.

"Someone has made us a gift," he said, "of a young retriever. One of the finest I have ever seen." He cleared his throat. "I really believe that Mariano and I could train him to be even as good as Don Polo's Lobo."

"You do?" asked 'Ama.

"I do," 'Apa replied.

Mariano's courage had returned.

"The truth?" he asked his father.

"I always tell the truth," his father answered.

RAMÓN'S NEW SHOES

Several months had passed since Ramón had begun to work at the hotel as a shoeshine boy. Evening after evening, with his new confidence and developed skills, the one peso notes and sometimes tips were coming his way. He was almost like a grown man, giving most of the money to his mother for the family support, and saving a little for himself.

At least once a week, he visited the leather shops. There were two of them in the town. Both of them were primarily engaged in leather working, the making of saddles and cheap sandals, but they did carry a few pairs of shoes. He was too shy to ask to be shown the shoes, rather he waited for customers to appear, and he watched and listened. On one occasion a boy just his size came in to one of the shops with his father and tried on a ninety-peso pair. Exactly what Ramón wanted, and the boy's father asked for something cheaper! Ramón watched the clerk replace the shoes in the box and put the box on a high shelf.

He ran home and counted his money. Eighty-nine pesos in all.

That night business was slow at the hotel. However, just before dinner was served, one guest came out of his room with three pairs of shoes to be shined. Ramón's ninety pesos were in hand. As he carefully worked over the shoes, he thought how he would look and feel tomorrow evening, entering the hotel wearing a brand-new pair all his own.

His work was soon done, and he grew impatient waiting for the guests to finish dinner. At eight-thirty the store would close, he knew, and he so wanted to take his new shoes home.

Finally the guests came out, and as he was being paid the church clock struck. The store would be closed until tomorrow. What with school, he would just have time to buy the shoes in the late afternoon, shine them, put them on and go to the hotel to work.

School, the next day, was an ordeal. Ramón paid no attention to the teacher whatsoever, and was subjected to scolding after scolding. Each time he tried to add a column, the figures blurred, and the pair of new shoes shone through.

Then the final bell rang. Holding one hand tightly over the pocket that contained the ninety pesos and carrying his shine box in the other, he ran to the leather shop. What if they had been sold? He tried not to think about it.

"I would like . . ." he gasped at the clerk, and pointed to the box on the high shelf.

"Those?" the clerk replied.

"Yes, yes. Those."

"But those are ninety pesos."

Ramón reached into his pocket and pulled out a thick wad of one-peso notes.

"Here," he said with self-assurance. Then, noticing the question still on the clerk's face, he added, "Count them."

And count them the clerk did. And there were exactly ninety pesos. He reached up to the shelf and withdrew the box.

"Don't you want to try them on?" he asked.

"Try them on? What for?"

"To see if they fit."

"They fit a boy who tried them on yesterday, and he's just my size, I know."

"I would suggest . . ." the clerk tried to plead his case.

"Please may I have them now," Ramón begged. "I am in a very great hurry."

"It won't take a minute," the clerk insisted. He opened the box, took out one shoe and knelt down. "Now," he said, "put your foot in here, slowly."

Impatient as he was, Ramón obeyed. It felt strange as the clerk laced up the shoe. Then the clerk eased his other foot into the other shoe and felt the toe with his thumb and squeezed the sides.

"You are right, young man," he agreed. "It's a perfect fit."

He watched Ramón's eyes move from one foot to the other.

"You'll want to wear them, I presume?"

"Yes, yes. Of course."

Ramón got up to leave.

"They may hurt a little, at first. This is true of all shoes. It takes . . ."

But Ramón was gone.

It was getting late. He hurried to the hotel, but his feet wouldn't move as fast as before. It was almost six when he hid himself in a dark corner of the arcade outside the hotel entry and proceeded to give himself a shine.

Then he stepped out into the light, admired himself.

"Now," he thought, "I am just like the *gente de razón,* important people!"

The shoes began to pinch his feet, and hurt. As he crossed the hotel patio to take his place, they hurt more and more, and made noise too, a squeaky, crunchy sound with every painful step.

When he was called by a guest, he hitched up his trousers so that his new shoes would show. He straddled his shinebox and stretched his legs out directly under the eyes of his customer. But somehow no one paid any attention to his feet.

Dinner was called. He watched the guests strolling toward the dining room, laughing, chatting, happy, no sign whatever of their feet hurting.

When he could leave, he suffered his way out of the hotel and to the corner of the arcade where the box was hidden. He had dreamed of walking home proudly, displaying his new prizes all the way. But he could stand it no longer.

He tried to get the shoes off. The knots in the laces held tight. The more he pulled, the tighter they got and the more they hurt. He crawled out into the light and vainly tried to untie the forced knots. He felt as though he were strangling. There was nothing left to do but cut the laces, new as they were, with the razor blade in his kit. And cut them he did. Slowly he extracted one squeezed foot after the other, and sighed, and stretched them, and wiggled his toes.

And as he walked home, the cool cobblestones soothed his bare feet. They began to return to normal, the pain was almost gone. He felt so good, that he began to wonder why the *gente de razón* wore shoes at all.

THE NEW HOUSE

Some months ago, Don Polo had decided that the Lopez family needed a new place to live. He knew that to repair the roof of the colonial ruin would be more costly than to construct a typical thatch-roof Indian cottage.

He and Juan had selected a piece of high ground, and he had marked out the floor plan and instructed Juan to supervise a few workmen, all he could afford. First, the adobe blocks had to be made from the heavy soil in the hollow by the *arroyo*. Then these were laid out to bake in the sun. Then, one row of blocks was placed describing the building. It was to be rectangular, with a curve at the far end.

Then workmen laid up the blocks to about four feet, leaving an opening in the front for a door.

Next, a ridge pole was set, and lighter-weight poles stretched out from it and overhung the walls by about two feet.

Then *carrizo*, a type of bamboo, was used for the cross members.

For several days Don Polo took the men and Juan in his truck up the hillside to a place where special palms grow, whose fronds are the best for the thatching.

Next, the palm thatch was laid on the skeleton and tied down with the tough slender leaves of the bamboo.

When the thatch reached the overhang of the building, a barbed-wire fence had to be set up all around to keep the burros and horses from eating the fresh greenery. After it dried, the animals lost interest and the fence could be removed.

Each late afternoon 'Ama would visit her new dwelling and imagine the comfort and security of a roof that did not leak.

Then came the great day. The new house was ready. The front extension, for cooking and eating and just sitting out and watching the moon come up over the sierra, had been roofed over. The fire-pit for cooking had been built.

'Apa had planned the move. For ten years they had lived in the same place. For ten years he had worked so hard, and he counted and recounted his possessions. Certainly a man who had worked so hard for so long would be possessed of a wealth of goods.

'Ama and the children had already carried the tin cans with the plants and flowers in them to the new place.

Don Polo had agreed to lend his truck for the major move, but on the prescribed day he had to leave for the Capital. 'Apa decided to wait until his return, but 'Ama, enthusiastic over the prospects of the new dwelling, urged that the move be made by hand. 'Apa finally agreed.

Each child was given something to carry, and the little procession made its way across the field bearing everything the family owned.

And as 'Apa realized how few possessions were his, how little in the way of belongings showed for his ten years of effort, he was saddened.

But as they reached the new house and put each thing in the place that 'Ama had selected, as the fire began to burn, as he began to smell the tortillas cooking and hear his children laughing and playing, he counted his blessings in his family, in their joy of living in their new home, and he asked only that he be given at least ten more years as profitable as those that had gone before.

"No, not this year. Definitely not," 'Apa determined to himself as he shoveled away some earth and let water run from the main canal to the lesser ones that fed the new crop of lemon trees. "Make a fool of myself again? Absolutely not."

It was the twenty-fourth of June, 'Apa's saint's day. And year after year on this day of San Juan, important because it traditionally brought with it the first rains of summer, 'Apa had joined other Juans of the community at the local cantina and ended up in jail. He was less disturbed by his vague drunken memories of the nights spent in confinement than he was by the vivid recollection of the coldness of his family, which lasted for several days after such event. He was a man of principle and determination, he told himself as he finished his afternoon's work and walked toward the shed to put the tools away. This evening he would celebrate quietly, and bask in the *felicitaciones* of his own children and wife.

Several Juans were waiting for him by the shed door, bottles of tequila in hand. Congratulations went the rounds, punctuated in each case by a swig from a bottle.

Out of courtesy, 'Apa drank.

"Come on, Juanito," the others urged him. "Just stopped by to get you and start the evening. Oh! lets make this the biggest one ever!"

"This time, I am sorry. I can't," said 'Apa, quietly.

"You always protest," was one reply.

"Every year, it's the same old thing. And every year you end up doing your little dance on the bandstand and they send us all to jail."

"But," protested 'Apa. He pointed toward the house. "*La vieja*—my old lady. This year, she made me promise!"

[71]

"Salud to your old lady!" cheered one of the Juans.

'Apa had to have a drink with each of them out of respect for 'Ama, if nothing else.

He was losing his convictions, however. He forced himself to say, "And now, with your permission, my good friends."

"Permission, my eye," another Juan protested. "What has happened to the Juan who held all women under his thumb. Are you to be ruled by a skirt?"

And then the deepest cut of all. "You, the one who used to be the most *macho* in the village, are you too old?"

The others chuckled.

'Apa slammed the door of the shed, grabbed the nearest bottle and drank deeply.

"Come on, my friends!" his voice rang loud. "Follow me."

He led them to the house.

"Woman," he said when he saw 'Ama. "I am the king. And the king is going with his friends to the cantina. And the king wants no word of protest. Now, I shall enter my castle so that each of you can *felicitarme,* and then off I go."

He moved toward the house. 'Ama hustled the children inside and locked the door behind her.

'Apa turned to his friends and gestured indifference. One of them handed him a bottle. And off they went, arm over shoulder, shouting the praises of each other.

Inside the house 'Ama made many excuses to the children for 'Apa's behavior. But within herself, despite ten years of repetition, she had never become accustomed nor resigned to 'Apa's being drunk. Her father was a chronic drinker, and sometimes mean, even cruel. Not that 'Apa had ever so behaved. But he was a man and he might, and this was her dread and the children sensed it.

It was difficult for her to calm them, to make them eat and then sleep, and it was long past their customary bedtime when they finally did fall away. She herself lay on her mat, praying for the safety of the man she loved.

A few hours later, still lying awake and waiting, 'Ama heard the strumming of a guitar. She peeked out through a crack in the door, and there was 'Apa bolstering himself up against a post and playing. Then he sang, sang the song that generations of serenaders have sung in the moonlight to their sweethearts, the song that he used to sing when he was courting her.

And 'Ama listened it through, and the deep lines of strife and work seemed to disappear from her face and the glow of youth in love returned.

She opened the door, when the song was done. She took the guitar from 'Apa's hands and laid it down. Gently she placed one of his arms over her shoulders, and she helped him stagger to his place beside her on the mat.

Then San Juan's Day rain came. Came with roars of thunder and bright, cold-blue flashes of lightning. Came with a downpour that roared its way into rivulets and ponds and streams down to the *arroyo*. But 'Apa slept, and the children slept.

'Ama lighted the lamp and inspected every corner of her new house. Not a leak. She passed the light over the faces of her sleeping children. She put out the light and lay down beside 'Apa, and worked her arm under his head and pressed him close to her breast.

'AMA'S PLANTS

It was early fall. The summer rains had been gener-
ous and the crops were good, and the Sierra was covered
with soft lacy green.

'Ama's plants had fared well. The consistent rains had
relieved her of the chore of carrying extra water from the
well to nurture them. And she was grateful for the re-
lief, for she was tired these days. It would not be long
before another member of the Lopez family would be
born. Extra money would be needed at least to feed the
extra hands that always come to help at childbirth, and
then there was the midwife as well.

She was glad when a buyer of plants from the city
drove up in his pickup.

"*Buenas tardes,* Señora." He doffed his hat a bit more
politely than usual, out of respect for 'Ama's condition.

"*Buenas tardes.*" 'Ama looked up from her work of
grinding corn.

"I see you have a new house."

"Yes, we do."

"A very nice one, too."

The buyer got out of his truck and began to inspect
the plants.

"Thank you," 'Ama replied. "We are very happy
with it. Even the roof holds off the rain."

"Nothing like the old-fashioned things, now is there?"

Then he got down to business. He pointed at a group
of purple bougainvillaeas.

"How much do these cost?" he asked.

"The purple ones?"

"Yes, the purple ones."

"Six pesos, each one."

"Six pesos, huh?"

'Ama didn't answer.

"And the orange ones?" the buyer queried.

"Eight pesos," 'Ama replied.

"Eight pesos." The buyer mulled over what he would offer. "And there, the *noche buenas?*"

"Twelve pesos." 'Ama continued grinding corn.

"Now," said the buyer. "We have four purple bougainvillaeas at six pesos. That's twenty-four. Six orange ones at eight pesos. That's forty-eight. And three *noche buenas* at twelve pesos. That's thirty-six. Let me see, now, twenty-four and forty-eight and thirty-six makes one hundred and eight pesos."

"Exactly one hundred and eight pesos," 'Ama agreed.

"And if I take them all, I presume . . ."

"If you take them all, it will be one hundred and eight pesos." 'Ama was firm.

The buyer, knowing that 'Ama would not budge, tried a new tack.

"This one here," he pointed to a plant with thin, tapered green leaves scattered with gold. "What do you call this?"

"Rain of Gold," 'Ama answered.

"It doesn't have flowers?"

"No."

"Then it must be cheap."

"It's not for sale." 'Ama stood up, her grinding was done.

"Does it bear fruit?"

The buyer was intrigued. He knew 'Ama would not lower her prices, but she might throw this one in if he took all the others.

"No, it does not bear fruit," 'Ama answered him.

Curiosity got the better of the buyer. "Then it must be rare."

"It is," 'Ama replied. "Rare enough to know that it can be beautiful without the weight of bearing flowers or fruits." She patted her protruding belly. "Only to have them fall and rot in the sun, or picked and carried away. No, it is not for sale."

Hurriedly the buyer paid her the one hundred and eight pesos and lifted his plants into the truck.

"Adiós, Señora." He started the motor and swung out of the driveway.

"Adiós." 'Ama could feel the movement of the new life within her. She reached out her hand and touched the leaf of the Rain of Gold. Then she spoke to it softly. "You will never know the anguish, nor will you ever know the joy."

She stood still for a moment, then shrugged her shoulders as though questioning her own statement, and then she turned back to the countless chores that awaited her.

JUANITO

'Apa was concerned with 'Ama's pregnancy, more so than he had been since her first. Vividly he remembered the fear and the excitement, the anticipation of having a first son, a Juanito. More vividly did he remember the terrible suffering of 'Ama, and finally the still-born child.

With all the others, it had been normal and comparatively easy, first Beatriz, then another boy. But superstition forbade the naming of him after his father. Where this concept came from, no one knew. Pride almost made 'Apa go against 'Ama's mother and the midwife. He had so wanted a son to bear the name of Juan Lopez. But weakly, he had agreed to name him Francisco — at least the nickname, Pancho, he had always liked.

Now 'Ama's pains were much the same as when she bore the long-since dead-and-buried first child. And 'Apa was greatly concerned.

He spoke to Don Polo about it, and of course he recommended that the new young doctor in town be brought into the case. 'Ama would have none of it. Hadn't she borne eight children safely and well, with only her mother and the midwife? Did 'Apa want her to expose her body to another man? Did he think she was a bad woman?

There was no answer to such arguments.

But, as the time grew closer, 'Ama's pains were greater than she could ever remember. Her mother moved into the house to help with the burden of work.

Then 'Ama went into the last labor. 'Apa was sent to bring the midwife.

Just as he started out, Don Polo's truck drove up. The new young doctor sat beside him.

"But you . . . you can't. She won't allow it," 'Apa protested.

"I'll take the blame." Don Polo crossed in front of 'Apa and urged the doctor into the house.

'Ama was practically unconscious, rolling convulsively on the straw mat. And before her mother could voice herself, the doctor was asking for hot water and towels. 'Apa stood by helplessly. Don Polo became the doctor's assistant.

The doctor examined his patient. He put on a pair of sterile gloves. He eased 'Ama's pain with a whiff of ether. He applied his forceps to the protruding head of the infant. He seemed to pull so hard that 'Apa turned away.

Then the doctor made an incision to increase the opening. Another pull, and out came a boy child, strangled by the cord. There was no cry.

Quickly the doctor cut the cord, tied it off, and began to apply mouth to mouth respiration. Minutes went by in the dark, silent little house. No noise but the gasping as the doctor took deep breaths. Still no infant cry.

The doctor called for a large bucket of cold water. He lowered the limp little body into it.

Then the cry came. The cry of defiance. The cry of life. And they dried the infant, and wrapped it warmly.

"There," said the doctor, as he laid it gently beside 'Ama. "There is your Juanito."

"They cannot call it Juanito," 'Ama's mother protested. "She lost the first one, you know."

"Yes, yes, I know. Don Polo has told me everything," the doctor replied. "But the way she has suffered with this one, and the struggle that he has made to come to life, I think he deserves the name."

"No! No!" Ama's mother went on. "Ill luck will befall him."

'Apa was right at the doctor's arm, urging him to press his point.

"My name is Juan," the doctor offered. "He has my breath in his lungs. Perhaps you would do me the honor . . .?"

"There's the solution." Don Polo settled the case. "Now, gentlemen, to my house to celebrate the birth."

The drinks were poured. 'Apa, sensing his importance in this situation, raised his glass and offered the toast, "To your," he nodded to the doctor, "and my, Juanito."

And as the young doctor held his glass to his lips, he began to think of his own past. He, too, had been born in a little house on a ranchito, twenty-eight years ago. His father had worked all his life for a man very much like the man now raising his glass in a toast. No doctor had brought him into the world. Mere chance, a rich uncle, had given him the opportunity for an education. His generation did not feel the push of the new era as strongly as it was being felt today. He was an exception.

Would this Juanito, he thought, owing his life to scientific knowledge, move forward into the stream of modernization, industrialization, mass production? Or would he be content to remain a part of this humble family?

Would he, in later life, be the father of his own *familia humilde?*

INHERIT THE EARTH was typeset and composed by Morneau Typographers of Phoenix in twelve-point Baskerville with two-point leading. The book was printed by F & S Phoenix on sixty-pound Nekoosa Ivory vellum, encased by the Arizona Trade Bindery in turquoise Joanna parchment linen. The jacket stock is Andorra white, from the Hamilton Paper Company.